# Tappety Drums

## Some useful hints

After making your first drum, make others using different materials for the 'skin'. Thin rubber sheeting, thin plastic sheeting, greaseproof paper, cartridge paper, vellum, strong brown wrapping paper and even burst balloons would be suitable.

Why do all these materials make different sounds when used on the drums?

Make some drums using longer cardboard tubes . . . these will also sound differently from the short ones.

Instead of cardboard tubes, the drums could be made by using empty tin cans (as long as they have a safe edge) . . . cover the can with a layer of self-adhesive, colored paper such as Contak before decorating it.

A long cardboard tube could have a skin stretched over both ends. Fix a cord to the tube so that it can be hung around your neck, leaving both hands free.

# Tappety drums

**1**

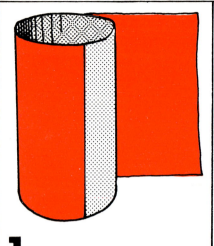

Cover a cardboard tube with colored paper.

**2**

Either stick on cut-out shapes or paint a pattern.

**3**

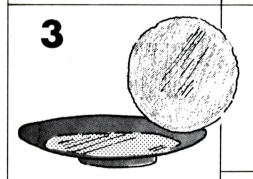

Dip a transparent, absorbent jar cover or filter paper in water.

**4**

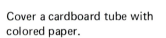

Put the damp cover on one end of the tube. Smooth tight.

**5**

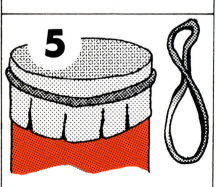

Fasten the cover with a rubber band.

**6**

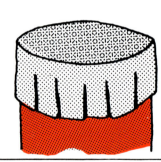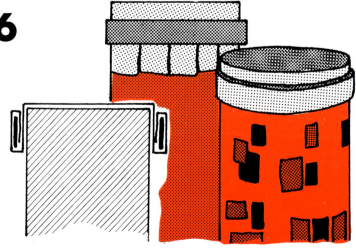

Another way is to use a wider rubber band and to tuck the cover neatly round it. Play the drum by tapping the cover with your fingers.

## Some useful hints

Thin rubber sheeting will give a better tone than plastic for the drum skin. Try other materials for the drum skin . . . test them by stretching them over the neck of an empty jam jar and tapping them gently with the fingers.

Find other containers which could be used for molds to make larger or differently shaped drums. Some plastic containers are suitable, but make sure that they have not been used for dangerous liquids (like bleach, for example).

Use strong, bright colors for decoration. How are real bongo drums decorated? Which country do they come from?

Use fringed braid to add the finishing touch to your model . . . put some glue on the back of the braid and tuck it underneath the rubber band.

When you paint the drums, first put on a layer of thick white paint. When this is dry, you can use the other colors, which will then look much brighter.

# Bongo drums

**1** Take a large and a small jar.

**2** Cover each with a layer of damp tissue paper.

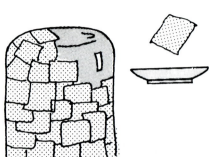

**3** Now add 8 layers of torn newspaper and paste. Smooth down well.

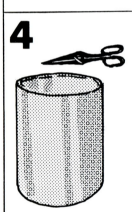

**4** When dry, take the paper shell off the jar and trim the end.

**5** Cut a wedge-shaped piece of wood.

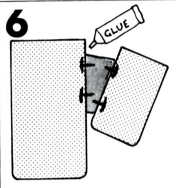

**6** Glue the paper shells to the wood. Hold in place from inside with thumb tacks.

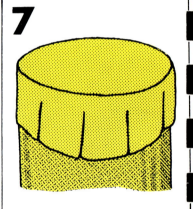

**7** Cover the open tops with thin plastic sheet.

**8** Fasten the cover with a wide rubber band (cut from an old inner tube).

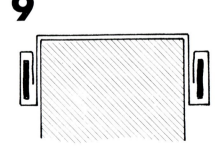

**9** Wrap the plastic sheet ends neatly round the rubber band.

**10** Paint the outer surface or decorate it with colored paper.

## Some useful hints

Paint the inside of the box as well as the outside — this helps to keep the cardboard flat.

Do not paint the top of the lid, since this may prevent the foam strip from sticking properly.

Try all sorts of different materials for the chime bars . . . aluminum, copper and steel tubing, electrical conduit, hollow brass curtain rods, steel strip, bamboo, strips of wood — even broken wooden and plastic rulers can be used.

To raise the pitch of the note, cut a little off the end of the tube.

To lower the pitch, cut a small notch in the center of the tube.

A wooden cigar box will make an excellent soundbox. Why is a wooden box better than one made of cardboard? Could you improve the tone from a shoe box by lining it with thin plywood?

# Xylophone or chime bar

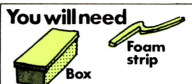

## You will need

Box

Foam strip

Brush handle

Large bead

Tubes or rods

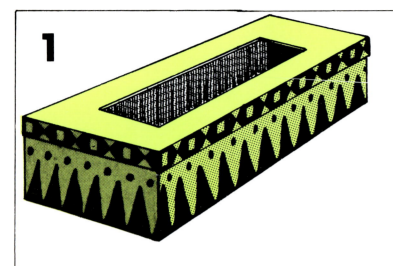

**1** Cut an opening in the lid of the box. Paint the sides.

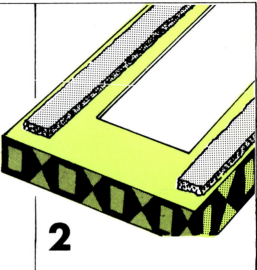

**2** Put two strips of self-adhesive foam or Polystyrene on the top of the box.

**3** Put short lengths of foam, leaving spaces between them, on top of the long strip.

**4** Make a hammer by gluing a large wooden or plastic bead to an old paintbrush handle.

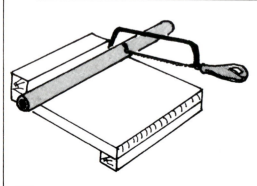

**5** Cut pieces of tube of different length.

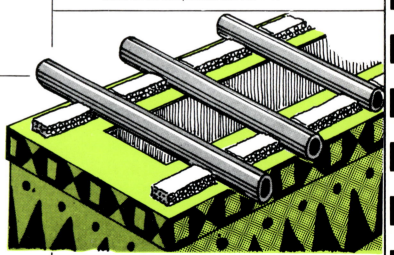

**6** Place the tubes between the raised foam spacers, in a graduated series according to length.

# CARD 4 | Tubular Chimes

## Some useful hints

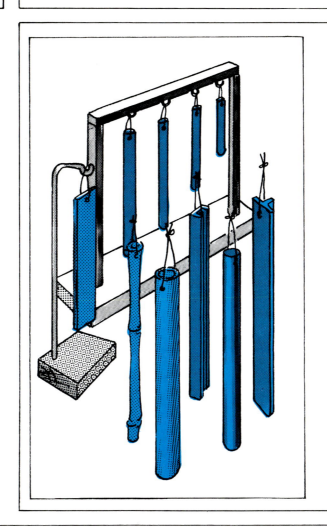

Hold the tube in a vice, or clamp it to a table, before drilling the holes for the string.
Try all sorts of things for the chimes . . . aluminum, copper and steel tube, angle iron, curtain rods, electrical conduit, bamboo, metal or wooden strips, old cutlery, and even slender glass bottles could be used.
The base for the stand could be cut from a plywood remnant or made from the end of an orange crate.
Why do different materials give different sounds?
Why does altering the length of the tube alter the pitch of the tone?
Instead of using string, the chimes could be hung up with picture wire or nylon cord.
Paint the stand with leftover wallpaint or oil paints. Polish the chimes with metal polish and then rub them with wax so that they keep their shine.

# Tubular chimes

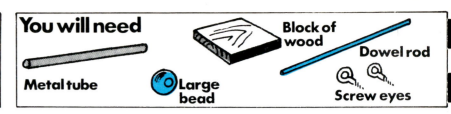

Metal tube  •  Large bead  •  Block of wood  •  Dowel rod  •  Screw eyes

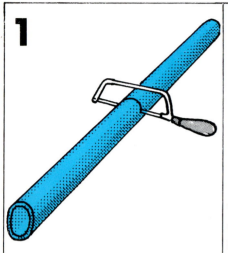

**1** Cut a tube into two unequal lengths.

**2** Drill or punch a small hole through one end of each tube.

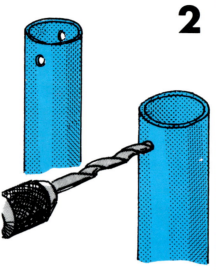

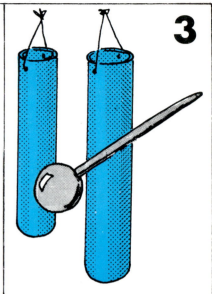

**3** Hang the tubes on thin wire or nylon cord and test the notes with the hammer.

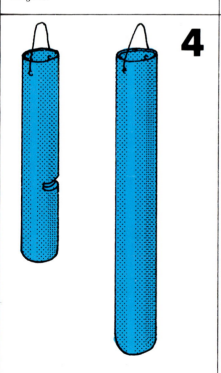

**4** Raise the pitch by cutting some off the end. Lower it by cutting a small slot in the tube.

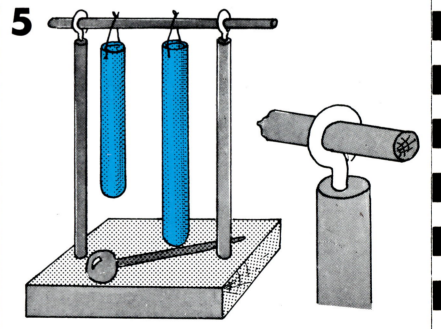

**5** With dowels and screw eyes, make a frame to support the chimes. Make a hammer from a large bead and an old paintbrush handle.

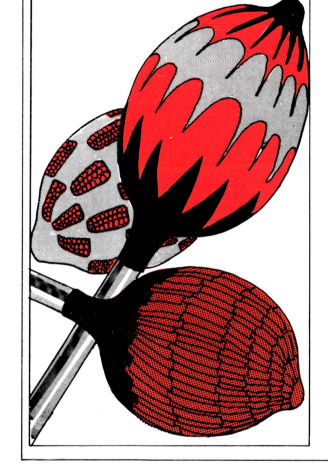

## Some useful hints

Instead of using plastic lemons, small plastic spice containers could be used for the maracas.

Make several maracas with a different filling in each so that you get different sounds.

Suitable fillings would be:— dried peas or corn kernels, split peas, rice, wheat, pebbles, small buttons, dry sand, small marbles or ball bearings.

Make sure that the handle is securely fixed to the plastic with strips of newspaper and paste. If it is loose, lively playing could send pebbles shooting all over the room!

After painting the finished maraca, add a coat of clear varnish or lacquer. This will give a finish which can be cleaned when it gets dirty.

Keep the decoration as simple as possible and use black and white highlights to get a bright effect.

Do not forget to wash your brush in clean water as soon as you have finished painting.

# Plastic maracas

**You will need**

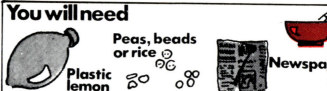
Plastic lemon

Peas, beads or rice

Newspaper

Paste

Dowel rod

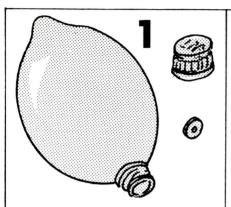

**1**

Remove the cap and plug from the plastic lemon.

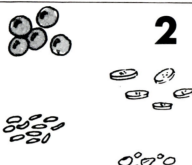

**2**

Drop in a few small hard objects.

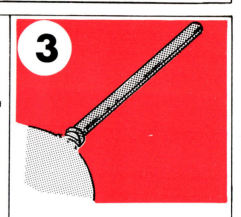

**3**

Push in a dowel rod to make a handle.

**4**

Put on 2 or 3 layers of torn newspaper and paste, covering part of the handle as well.

**5**

When dry, paint the maraca with thick watercolor or tempera.

**6**

Round and smooth the end of the handle with sandpaper.

**7**

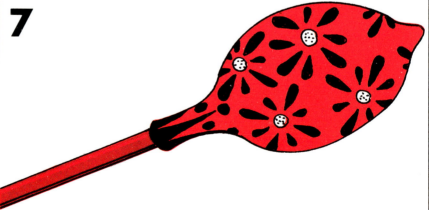

Decorate with a second color or Magic Marker, or by pasting on paper shapes.

| CARD | 6 | Zither |
|------|---|--------|

## Some useful hints

Instead of screw eyes, proper wrest pins could be used to secure the strings. These can be purchased from larger music stores or obtained from an old piano.

The plywood for the top should be as thin as possible or the tone from the zither will be rather dead.

The zither is normally played by plucking the strings, but you could try making a simple bow from a length of bamboo and fishing line. Using the bow will give a different effect with sustained notes.

Before painting the outside of the box, paint the inside . . .this will help to stop the sides of the box from curling.

If you are able to make a wooden box with a plywood top and bottom, this will give a better tone than the cardboard box.

Use the zither on a table rather than held in your hands, because the tabletop acts as a sounding board and improves the tone.

# THE WEDDING OF:

&

Help us to improve this planner, so we can help other brides and grooms in the future.
Please submit your suggestions to info@yourperfectday.com

# FROM US...
# TO YOU...

Congratulations on getting engaged. We are so delighted for you and can't wait to help and support you with your planning journey. Now sit back and relax, planning your dream wedding doesn't have to be anywhere near as stressful as you may think.

You are about to embark on one of the most fun and rewarding journeys in your life. Just imagine, all of your friends, family and loved ones together to celebrate you and your beloved making a lifelong commitment to one another.

Planning your wedding can seem overwhelming but we are here to help and support you. We've created this simple and easy to follow wedding planner based on our own experience of planning many weddings all over the world.

This planner will help you organize and document your entire wedding and even serves as a great keepsake for storing your wedding memories. Each and every section in this planner has been designed to give you guidance whilst giving you flexibility to make your own notes and suggestions as no two weddings are ever the same.

We've included some really handy tips and hints from other experienced wedding planners and former brides that should make planning Your Perfect Day a lot easier.

We've also created some really simple online templates that you can easily download to help you along your wedding planning journey.

Remember – there's no right and wrong time to do any of the tasks. You may be super keen and want to jump ahead to sections, or leaving it late and trying to squeeze everything in at the last minute.

When planning Your Perfect Day, just remember to stay calm, stick to your vision and keep a track of your budgets. The rest will just fall into place.

Enjoy planning, we are here with you every step of the way.

*Lottie*

Wedding & Event Planner
Co-Founder of YourPerfectDay.com

# CONTENTS

## YOUR WEDDING VISION

Use this section to get creative and set the tone for your wedding. Print out pictures, stick in bridal magazine cutouts, add images from Pinterest, fabric swatches and more to create your vision boards. These act as a visual reference for the key elements in your day.

## FUNDAMENTALS & TIMELINE

This section is your main wedding planning section. Firstly choose your bridal party and set your budget. Track all of your key dates and milestones with your countdown calendar.

## GUEST PLANNING

This section will help you keep track of who has been invited, who is attending and is also handy to track any gifts received from your guests.

# VENUES & VENDORS

This section will help you to keep track of all of your vendors, your chosen wedding venue(s), hotels and guest accommodation.

- ♡ Choosing Your Wedding Venue
- ♡ Wedding Venue Shortlist
- ♡ Guest Accommodation
- ♡ Choosing Your Wedding Vendors
- ♡ Choosing Your Photographer / Videographer
- ♡ Questions for the Photographer
- ♡ Questions for the Videographer
- ♡ The Dress
- ♡ Bridesmaid's Dresses
- ♡ Groom's Outfit
- ♡ Caterers
- ♡ Florist / Floral Designer
- ♡ Wedding Cake
- ♡ Wedding Hair

- ♡ Wedding Make Up
- ♡ Beauty Treatments
- ♡ The Officiant
- ♡ Wedding Transport
- ♡ Entertainment
- ♡ Favors
- ♡ Wedding Bands
- ♡ Stationery
- ♡ Your Wedding Website
- ♡ Additional Vendor Info
- ♡ Researching Honeymoon Destinations
- ♡ Honeymoon Notes
- ♡ Notes
- ♡ To Do

# OUR WEDDING DAY

This section includes all of the useful info for you in the run up to your wedding and your wedding day. Keep track of your readings, music choices, itinerary and more.

- ♡ Readings
- ♡ Music Choices
- ♡ Creating Your Photography List
- ♡ Sample Itinerary
- ♡ Our Itinerary

- ♡ Wedding Day Survival Kit
- ♡ Honeymoon Packing Checklist
- ♡ Your Vows
- ♡ Notes
- ♡ Last Minute To Dos
- ♡ Ready, Steady, Wed!

# DISCUSS YOUR WEDDING DAY WITH YOUR PARTNER

YOUR IDEAS

# DISCUSS YOUR WEDDING DAY WITH YOUR PARTNER

## YOUR PARTNERS' IDEAS

# YOUR CEREMONY
## VISION BOARD
**Visualize your perfect wedding ceremony**

# YOUR RECEPTION
## VISION BOARD
**Visualize your perfect wedding reception**

# YOUR GOWN
# & ACCESSORIES
## VISION BOARD
**Visualize your wedding outfit**

# GROOM'S OUTFIT

## VISION BOARD

**Visualize how the groom will look on your wedding day**

# BRIDAL PARTY
## VISION BOARD
**Visualize how your bridal party will look and what they will wear**

# TRANSPORT & ACCOMMODATION

## VISION BOARD

**Visualize your wedding transport and guest accommodation**

# CAKE & CATERING

## VISION BOARD

**Visualize how you want food to be served and how it will look**

# MAKE UP & BEAUTY
## VISION BOARD
**Visualize how you will look on your wedding day**

# YOUR HONEYMOON

## VISION BOARD

**Visualize your perfect honeymoon**

# INSPIRATION
## VISION BOARD
**Visualize other inspirational elements for your perfect day**

# CHOOSE YOUR
# BRIDAL PARTY

Whilst the two of you are the most important people on your wedding day, having your closest friends and family around you will make the day even more special. Being a bridesmaid or groomsman is a privilege but comes with responsibility, so make sure you choose wisely from your friends, siblings and extended family.

| Maid of Honor | Best Man |
|---|---|
| | |

### Bridesmaid(s)

1 _____
2 _____
3 _____
4 _____
5 _____
6 _____
7 _____
8 _____

### Usher(s)

_____
_____
_____
_____
_____
_____
_____
_____

### Flower Girl(s)

1 _____
2 _____
3 _____
4 _____

### Ring Bearer(s)

_____
_____
_____
_____

# SET YOUR BUDGET

Whilst tradition says that certain people pay for different wedding costs, the reality is much different now.

More and more couples are paying for large parts of the wedding themselves, with the support of family and friends helping out where possible.

It is a good idea to speak with your family about your wedding plans as early as possible. Mention how much you are looking to spend and ask them if they are willing (if able) to help contribute to your special day.

This handy budget planner should help you keep track of what things are going to cost.

## REMEMBER

Who pays for what is more of a guideline than a set of rules. Each family will have their own financial circumstances to take into consideration.

## TIP:

Set a contingency of 10% for unexpected surprises. E.g. If you have a $30,000 budget, try and keep to a budget of $27,000.

If you can keep under budget throughout the planning process you'll have some saved money that you can use for your honeymoon or to put towards your home.

## NOTE:

We realize costs change in the run up to your wedding and keeping track can be a challenge. Feel free to download any of our templates online at YourPerfectDay.com/templates

# WHO TRADITIONALLY PAYS FOR WHAT?

## CEREMONY

| | |
|---|---|
| Church / Synagogue / Sexton / Organist etc. | Bride & Family |
| Marriage Licence & Officiant Fee | Groom & Family |

## WEDDING ATTIRE

| | |
|---|---|
| Dress & Accessories | Bride & Family |
| Groom's Outfit | Groom & Family |

## FLOWERS AND DECORATIONS

| | |
|---|---|
| Bride's Bouquet, Boutonnières / Corsages | Groom & Family |
| All Other Flowers | Bride & Family |

## HONEYMOON

Groom & Family

## PHOTOGRAPHY / VIDEO

Bride & Family

## PRE-PARTIES

| | |
|---|---|
| Engagement Party | Bride or Groom's Family |
| Rehearsal Dinner | Groom's Family |
| Bachelorette Party | Maid of Honor & Bridesmaids |
| Bachelor Party | Best Man & Groomsmen |

## RECEPTION

| | |
|---|---|
| Other costs including Catering | Bride & Family |
| DJ / Band / Liquor | Bride & Family |

## RINGS

| | |
|---|---|
| Groom's Ring | Bride & Family |
| Bride's Ring | Groom & Family |

## STATIONERY

Bride & Family

## WEDDING TRANSPORT

Bride & Family

# BUDGET PLANNER

| ITEM | BUDGET | ACTUAL | NOTES |
|------|--------|--------|-------|
| **Ceremony / Reception** | Budget | Actual | Notes |
| Venue / Marquee Rental | | | |
| Reception Catering | | | |
| Evening Catering | | | |
| Drinks | | | |
| Cake | | | |
| Confetti | | | |
| Décor | | | |
| **Wedding Attire** | Budget | Actual | Notes |
| Wedding Dress | | | |
| Dress Alterations | | | |
| Veil | | | |
| Jewelry | | | |
| Wedding Shoes | | | |
| Accessories | | | |
| Groom's Suit | | | |
| Groom's Shoes | | | |
| Bridesmaid's Dresses | | | |
| Groomsmen Suits | | | |
| Flower Girl Outfits | | | |
| Ring Bearer Outfit(s) | | | |
| Groom's Accessories | | | |
| **Beauty** | Budget | Actual | Notes |
| Hair Trial | | | |
| Hair | | | |
| Make Up Trial | | | |
| Make Up | | | |
| **Entertainment** | Budget | Actual | Notes |
| Live Band | | | |
| DJ | | | |
| Magicians | | | |
| Musicians | | | |
| Sound System | | | |
| Dance Floor | | | |
| Party Accessories | | | |
| Sweet Cart / Table | | | |
| **Décor & Dressing** | Budget | Actual | Notes |
| Floral Designer | | | |
| Wedding Flowers | | | |
| Centrepieces | | | |
| Lighting | | | |
| Table Décor | | | |
| Ceremony Décor | | | |
| Corsages / Buttonholes | | | |

| ITEM | BUDGET | ACTUAL | NOTES |
|---|---|---|---|

| Capturing The Day | Budget | Actual | Notes |
|---|---|---|---|
| Photographer | | | |
| Videographer | | | |
| Wedding Album | | | |

| Communications & Stationery | Budget | Actual | Notes |
|---|---|---|---|
| Engagement Party Invites | | | |
| Save The Date Cards | | | |
| Bridal Shower Invites | | | |
| Bachelor/ette Invitations | | | |
| Wedding Invitations | | | |
| Ceremony Programs | | | |
| Place / Escort Cards | | | |
| Table Number Cards | | | |
| Menu Cards | | | |
| Favor Cards | | | |
| Thank You Cards | | | |
| Wedding Website | | | |

| Transport | Budget | Actual | Notes |
|---|---|---|---|
| Wedding Car Bride / Groom | | | |
| Wedding Cars Groomsmen / Bridesmaids | | | |
| Coach / Bus Rental for Bridal Party | | | |

| Rings | Budget | Actual | Notes |
|---|---|---|---|
| Wedding Ring Bride | | | |
| Wedding Ring Groom | | | |
| Gifts | | | |
| Wedding Favors | | | |
| Bridesmaid's Gifts | | | |
| Groomsmen Gifts | | | |
| Parent's Gifts | | | |
| Flower Girl / Ring Bearer Gifts | | | |

| Miscellaneous | Budget | Actual | Notes |
|---|---|---|---|
| Wedding Insurance | | | |

ADD STUFF HERE

TIP:

Go through your list of friends and family. Are there any guests that are to be invited that can help? An Auntie that bakes, a cousin that is an expert in flower arranging? Often personal gifts are more appreciated and they can help you keep on budget.

# WEDDING COUNTDOWN

## 12 MONTHS+ TO GO

- ☐ Visit ceremony & reception venues
- ☐ Choose your bridal party
- ☐ Write your guest list
- ☐ Secure your chosen venue and wedding date
- ☐ Arrange to meet with officiant
- ☐ Research and meet vendors
- ☐ Pre-book any 'in demand' vendors
- ☐ Work out your budget
- ☐ Pick a date for your engagement party

## 10-11 MONTHS TO GO

- ☐ Send your save the date cards
- ☐ Book vendors
- ☐ Organize an evening out with your bridal party
- ☐ Set up a simple wedding website
- ☐ Research guest accommodation
- ☐ Visit dress stores for dress ideas
- ☐ Discuss and research honeymoon destinations
- ☐ Start researching bridesmaid dress options
- ☐ Choose your outfit

## 7-9 MONTHS TO GO

- ☐ Book your caterer
- ☐ Book any transport
- ☐ Book your florist / floral designer
- ☐ Book wedding entertainment
- ☐ Book all other vendors for daytime and evening entertainment
- ☐ Order wedding cake
- ☐ Order your wedding dress & accessories
- ☐ Order your bridesmaid dresses
- ☐ Book accommodation for your first night as newlyweds
- ☐ Decide on wedding favors

# 5-6 MONTHS TO GO

- ☐ Write your gift list
- ☐ Shop for wedding rings
- ☐ Book your honeymoon
- ☐ Organize groom's outfit
- ☐ Organize your groomsman outfits
- ☐ Decide on gifts for the bridal party
- ☐ Design all other stationery

- ☐ Order passports (if needed)
- ☐ Send your bachelorette and bachelor guest list to those organizing the events
- ☐ Book hair and make-up trial
- ☐ Organize food tasting with vendor
- ☐ Confirm final menu choices
- ☐ Book rehearsal dinner

# 3-4 MONTHS TO GO

- ☐ Order wedding stationery
- ☐ Buy outfits for honeymoon
- ☐ Purchase or make decorations for the day
- ☐ Send formal wedding invites
- ☐ Buy gifts for the bridal party / parents
- ☐ Book beauty treatments & trials
- ☐ Gifts for the bride and groom

- ☐ Wedding dress fitting
- ☐ Pick music choices
- ☐ Decide on readings and who is doing them
- ☐ Create wedding playlist / choose DJ
- ☐ Write your shot list for the photographer
- ☐ Pick lingerie and jewelry

# 2 MONTHS TO GO

- ☐ Draft seating plan
- ☐ Write vows (if needed)
- ☐ Remind groom to write his speech
- ☐ Enjoy bachelorette and bachelor parties

- ☐ Book wedding rehearsal
- ☐ Write your wedding day itinerary
- ☐ Organize travel insurance

# 1 MONTH TO GO

- ☐ Final wedding gown fitting
- ☐ Confirm wedding transport
- ☐ Confirm final numbers with the wedding venue and vendors
- ☐ Check your vendors have everything they need
- ☐ Confirm final dietary requirements
- ☐ Apply for marriage licence
- ☐ Buy wedding guest book
- ☐ Finalise the seating plan
- ☐ Pick up marriage licence
- ☐ Create photography list
- ☐ Check all RSVPs and re-confirm if anyone hasn't confirmed
- ☐ Give shot list to photographer
- ☐ Arrange welcome bags for traveling guests

# YOUR FINAL WEEK

- ☐ Confirm responsibilities with ushers, bridesmaids, family
- ☐ Re-confirm everything with vendors
- ☐ Print your itinerary and timings for the day
- ☐ Print your honeymoon travel documents
- ☐ Order travel currency for honeymoon (if going overseas)
- ☐ Prepare your wedding day survival kit
- ☐ Rehearsal for ceremony
- ☐ Pack your honeymoon bags
- ☐ Pamper and try to relax
- ☐ Write out list of vendors and give to appropriate people
- ☐ Get your wedding dress pressed
- ☐ Write any 'thank you' notes
- ☐ Pick up groomsman / groom suits

# DAY BEFORE

- ☐ Give vendors contact details to each other
- ☐ Write out any checks
- ☐ Enjoy your rehearsal dinner
- ☐ Present marriage licence to officiant
- ☐ Try not to over-indulge so you are fresh for your big day tomorrow
- ☐ Enjoy yourself

# COUNTDOWN CALENDAR

MONTH:

| Monday | Tuesday | Wednesday | Thursday | Friday | Saturday | Sunday |
|--------|---------|-----------|----------|--------|----------|--------|
|        |         |           |          |        |          |        |
|        |         |           |          |        |          |        |

# COUNTDOWN CALENDAR

## MONTH:

| Monday | Tuesday | Wednesday | Thursday | Friday | Saturday | Sunday |
|--------|---------|-----------|----------|--------|----------|--------|
|        |         |           |          |        |          |        |
|        |         |           |          |        |          |        |

# COUNTDOWN CALENDAR

## MONTH:

| Monday | Tuesday | Wednesday | Thursday | Friday | Saturday | Sunday |
|--------|---------|-----------|----------|--------|----------|--------|
|        |         |           |          |        |          |        |
|        |         |           |          |        |          |        |

# COUNTDOWN CALENDAR

## MONTH:

| Monday | Tuesday | Wednesday | Thursday | Friday | Saturday | Sunday |
|--------|---------|-----------|----------|--------|----------|--------|
|        |         |           |          |        |          |        |
|        |         |           |          |        |          |        |

# COUNTDOWN CALENDAR

## MONTH:

| Monday | Tuesday | Wednesday | Thursday | Friday | Saturday | Sunday |
|--------|---------|-----------|----------|--------|----------|--------|
|        |         |           |          |        |          |        |
|        |         |           |          |        |          |        |

# COUNTDOWN CALENDAR

## MONTH:

| Monday | Tuesday | Wednesday | Thursday | Friday | Saturday | Sunday |
|--------|---------|-----------|----------|--------|----------|--------|
|        |         |           |          |        |          |        |
|        |         |           |          |        |          |        |

# COUNTDOWN CALENDAR

## MONTH:

| Monday | Tuesday | Wednesday | Thursday | Friday | Saturday | Sunday |
|--------|---------|-----------|----------|--------|----------|--------|
|        |         |           |          |        |          |        |
|        |         |           |          |        |          |        |

# COUNTDOWN CALENDAR

## MONTH:

| Monday | Tuesday | Wednesday | Thursday | Friday | Saturday | Sunday |
|--------|---------|-----------|----------|--------|----------|--------|
| | | | | | | |
| | | | | | | |

# COUNTDOWN CALENDAR

## MONTH:

| Monday | Tuesday | Wednesday | Thursday | Friday | Saturday | Sunday |
|--------|---------|-----------|----------|--------|----------|--------|
|        |         |           |          |        |          |        |
|        |         |           |          |        |          |        |

# COUNTDOWN CALENDAR

## MONTH:

| Monday | Tuesday | Wednesday | Thursday | Friday | Saturday | Sunday |
|--------|---------|-----------|----------|--------|----------|--------|
|        |         |           |          |        |          |        |
|        |         |           |          |        |          |        |

# COUNTDOWN CALENDAR

MONTH:

| Monday | Tuesday | Wednesday | Thursday | Friday | Saturday | Sunday |
|--------|---------|-----------|----------|--------|----------|--------|
|        |         |           |          |        |          |        |
|        |         |           |          |        |          |        |

# COUNTDOWN CALENDAR

MONTH:

| Monday | Tuesday | Wednesday | Thursday | Friday | Saturday | Sunday |
|--------|---------|-----------|----------|--------|----------|--------|
|        |         |           |          |        |          |        |
|        |         |           |          |        |          |        |

# COUNTDOWN CALENDAR

## MONTH:

| Monday | Tuesday | Wednesday | Thursday | Friday | Saturday | Sunday |
|--------|---------|-----------|----------|--------|----------|--------|
|        |         |           |          |        |          |        |
|        |         |           |          |        |          |        |

# COUNTDOWN CALENDAR

## MONTH:

| Monday | Tuesday | Wednesday | Thursday | Friday | Saturday | Sunday |
|--------|---------|-----------|----------|--------|----------|--------|
| | | | | | | |
| | | | | | | |

# COUNTDOWN CALENDAR

MONTH:

| Monday | Tuesday | Wednesday | Thursday | Friday | Saturday | Sunday |
|--------|---------|-----------|----------|--------|----------|--------|
|        |         |           |          |        |          |        |
|        |         |           |          |        |          |        |

# COUNTDOWN CALENDAR

## MONTH:

| Monday | Tuesday | Wednesday | Thursday | Friday | Saturday | Sunday |
|--------|---------|-----------|----------|--------|----------|--------|
|        |         |           |          |        |          |        |
|        |         |           |          |        |          |        |

# COUNTDOWN CALENDAR

## MONTH:

| Monday | Tuesday | Wednesday | Thursday | Friday | Saturday | Sunday |
|--------|---------|-----------|----------|--------|----------|--------|
|        |         |           |          |        |          |        |
|        |         |           |          |        |          |        |

# COUNTDOWN CALENDAR

## MONTH:

| Monday | Tuesday | Wednesday | Thursday | Friday | Saturday | Sunday |
|--------|---------|-----------|----------|--------|----------|--------|
|        |         |           |          |        |          |        |
|        |         |           |          |        |          |        |

# NOTES

# NOTES

# NOTES

# NOTES

# NOTES

# NOTES

# GUEST PLANNING

This section will help you keep track of who has been invited,
who is attending and is also handy to track any gifts received
from your guests.

# WEDDING GUEST LIST ETIQUETTE

The biggest thing that will determine the size of your guest list is your budget.

Once you have worked out how much you have to spend on your wedding, you can decide on the number of people you can afford to invite.

Remember about 5% of people will not be able to attend. Don't rely on people not being able to attend your wedding, invite just the number of guests that you can afford.

Start by writing down a list of your "must have" guests. This will include close family and close friends and work it from there.

## FRIENDS & FAMILY

- ♡ Parents
- ♡ Siblings, Aunts, Uncles, and First Cousins
- ♡ Are You Inviting Second Cousins?
- ♡ Are You Inviting Third cousins?

## WORK

- ♡ Co-Workers
- ♡ Business Partners
- ♡ Clients / Vendors
- ♡ Do you want to invite all co-workers? Could you save money by inviting them to the evening only?

## FRIENDS

- ♡ Best Friends
- ♡ Childhood Friends
- ♡ Partners Of Friends
- ♡ Church Friends / Religious Groups
- ♡ Community Friends

## OTHERS

- ♡ What Is Your +1 Policy? (Have they been together more than a year?)
- ♡ Neighbors?
- ♡ Mentors
- ♡ Parents' Friends?
- ♡ What Is Your Kids Policy?

## MONEY SAVING TIP:

Deciding on what guests to invite is one of the hardest tasks on your wedding day. If your costs are getting high remember you can always invite guests to your evening reception. An evening meal is typically less expensive than a meal at the wedding reception, plus you aren't obliged to pay for their drinks too.

Remember, people will be thrilled to be invited to your wedding, regardless of whether it is to the evening or the whole day.

# YOUR GUEST LIST

This handy guest list can also double up as a gift list to keep track of what you have received.

**NOTE:**

We realize guest lists change throughout the wedding planning process and keeping track can be a challenge. Feel free to download any of our templates online at YourPerfectDay.com/templates

| NAME | DAY GUEST | EVENING GUEST | SAVE THE DATE SENT | INVITE SENT | ATTENDING | GIFT |
|---|---|---|---|---|---|---|
| | ☐ | ☐ | ☐ | ☐ | ☐ | |
| | ☐ | ☐ | ☐ | ☐ | ☐ | |
| | ☐ | ☐ | ☐ | ☐ | ☐ | |
| | ☐ | ☐ | ☐ | ☐ | ☐ | |
| | ☐ | ☐ | ☐ | ☐ | ☐ | |
| | ☐ | ☐ | ☐ | ☐ | ☐ | |
| | ☐ | ☐ | ☐ | ☐ | ☐ | |
| | ☐ | ☐ | ☐ | ☐ | ☐ | |
| | ☐ | ☐ | ☐ | ☐ | ☐ | |
| | ☐ | ☐ | ☐ | ☐ | ☐ | |
| | ☐ | ☐ | ☐ | ☐ | ☐ | |
| | ☐ | ☐ | ☐ | ☐ | ☐ | |
| | ☐ | ☐ | ☐ | ☐ | ☐ | |
| | ☐ | ☐ | ☐ | ☐ | ☐ | |
| | ☐ | ☐ | ☐ | ☐ | ☐ | |
| | ☐ | ☐ | ☐ | ☐ | ☐ | |
| | ☐ | ☐ | ☐ | ☐ | ☐ | |
| | ☐ | ☐ | ☐ | ☐ | ☐ | |
| | ☐ | ☐ | ☐ | ☐ | ☐ | |
| | ☐ | ☐ | ☐ | ☐ | ☐ | |
| | ☐ | ☐ | ☐ | ☐ | ☐ | |
| | ☐ | ☐ | ☐ | ☐ | ☐ | |
| | ☐ | ☐ | ☐ | ☐ | ☐ | |
| | ☐ | ☐ | ☐ | ☐ | ☐ | |
| | ☐ | ☐ | ☐ | ☐ | ☐ | |
| | ☐ | ☐ | ☐ | ☐ | ☐ | |
| | ☐ | ☐ | ☐ | ☐ | ☐ | |
| | ☐ | ☐ | ☐ | ☐ | ☐ | |
| | ☐ | ☐ | ☐ | ☐ | ☐ | |

| NAME | DAY GUEST | EVENING GUEST | SAVE THE DATE SENT | INVITE SENT | ATTENDING | GIFT |
|------|-----------|---------------|--------------------|-------------|-----------|------|
|  | ☐ | ☐ | ☐ | ☐ | ☐ |  |
|  | ☐ | ☐ | ☐ | ☐ | ☐ |  |
|  | ☐ | ☐ | ☐ | ☐ | ☐ |  |
|  | ☐ | ☐ | ☐ | ☐ | ☐ |  |
|  | ☐ | ☐ | ☐ | ☐ | ☐ |  |
|  | ☐ | ☐ | ☐ | ☐ | ☐ |  |
|  | ☐ | ☐ | ☐ | ☐ | ☐ |  |
|  | ☐ | ☐ | ☐ | ☐ | ☐ |  |
|  | ☐ | ☐ | ☐ | ☐ | ☐ |  |
|  | ☐ | ☐ | ☐ | ☐ | ☐ |  |
|  | ☐ | ☐ | ☐ | ☐ | ☐ |  |
|  | ☐ | ☐ | ☐ | ☐ | ☐ |  |
|  | ☐ | ☐ | ☐ | ☐ | ☐ |  |
|  | ☐ | ☐ | ☐ | ☐ | ☐ |  |
|  | ☐ | ☐ | ☐ | ☐ | ☐ |  |
|  | ☐ | ☐ | ☐ | ☐ | ☐ |  |
|  | ☐ | ☐ | ☐ | ☐ | ☐ |  |
|  | ☐ | ☐ | ☐ | ☐ | ☐ |  |
|  | ☐ | ☐ | ☐ | ☐ | ☐ |  |
|  | ☐ | ☐ | ☐ | ☐ | ☐ |  |
|  | ☐ | ☐ | ☐ | ☐ | ☐ |  |
|  | ☐ | ☐ | ☐ | ☐ | ☐ |  |
|  | ☐ | ☐ | ☐ | ☐ | ☐ |  |
|  | ☐ | ☐ | ☐ | ☐ | ☐ |  |
|  | ☐ | ☐ | ☐ | ☐ | ☐ |  |
|  | ☐ | ☐ | ☐ | ☐ | ☐ |  |
|  | ☐ | ☐ | ☐ | ☐ | ☐ |  |
|  | ☐ | ☐ | ☐ | ☐ | ☐ |  |
|  | ☐ | ☐ | ☐ | ☐ | ☐ |  |
|  | ☐ | ☐ | ☐ | ☐ | ☐ |  |
|  | ☐ | ☐ | ☐ | ☐ | ☐ |  |
|  | ☐ | ☐ | ☐ | ☐ | ☐ |  |
|  | ☐ | ☐ | ☐ | ☐ | ☐ |  |
|  | ☐ | ☐ | ☐ | ☐ | ☐ |  |
|  | ☐ | ☐ | ☐ | ☐ | ☐ |  |
|  | ☐ | ☐ | ☐ | ☐ | ☐ |  |
|  | ☐ | ☐ | ☐ | ☐ | ☐ |  |

| NAME | DAY GUEST | EVENING GUEST | SAVE THE DATE SENT | INVITE SENT | ATTENDING | GIFT |
|------|-----------|---------------|--------------------|-------------|-----------|------|
| | ☐ | ☐ | ☐ | ☐ | ☐ | |
| | ☐ | ☐ | ☐ | ☐ | ☐ | |
| | ☐ | ☐ | ☐ | ☐ | ☐ | |
| | ☐ | ☐ | ☐ | ☐ | ☐ | |
| | ☐ | ☐ | ☐ | ☐ | ☐ | |
| | ☐ | ☐ | ☐ | ☐ | ☐ | |
| | ☐ | ☐ | ☐ | ☐ | ☐ | |
| | ☐ | ☐ | ☐ | ☐ | ☐ | |
| | ☐ | ☐ | ☐ | ☐ | ☐ | |
| | ☐ | ☐ | ☐ | ☐ | ☐ | |
| | ☐ | ☐ | ☐ | ☐ | ☐ | |
| | ☐ | ☐ | ☐ | ☐ | ☐ | |
| | ☐ | ☐ | ☐ | ☐ | ☐ | |
| | ☐ | ☐ | ☐ | ☐ | ☐ | |
| | ☐ | ☐ | ☐ | ☐ | ☐ | |
| | ☐ | ☐ | ☐ | ☐ | ☐ | |
| | ☐ | ☐ | ☐ | ☐ | ☐ | |
| | ☐ | ☐ | ☐ | ☐ | ☐ | |
| | ☐ | ☐ | ☐ | ☐ | ☐ | |
| | ☐ | ☐ | ☐ | ☐ | ☐ | |
| | ☐ | ☐ | ☐ | ☐ | ☐ | |
| | ☐ | ☐ | ☐ | ☐ | ☐ | |
| | ☐ | ☐ | ☐ | ☐ | ☐ | |
| | ☐ | ☐ | ☐ | ☐ | ☐ | |
| | ☐ | ☐ | ☐ | ☐ | ☐ | |
| | ☐ | ☐ | ☐ | ☐ | ☐ | |
| | ☐ | ☐ | ☐ | ☐ | ☐ | |
| | ☐ | ☐ | ☐ | ☐ | ☐ | |
| | ☐ | ☐ | ☐ | ☐ | ☐ | |
| | ☐ | ☐ | ☐ | ☐ | ☐ | |
| | ☐ | ☐ | ☐ | ☐ | ☐ | |
| | ☐ | ☐ | ☐ | ☐ | ☐ | |
| | ☐ | ☐ | ☐ | ☐ | ☐ | |
| | ☐ | ☐ | ☐ | ☐ | ☐ | |
| | ☐ | ☐ | ☐ | ☐ | ☐ | |
| | ☐ | ☐ | ☐ | ☐ | ☐ | |
| | ☐ | ☐ | ☐ | ☐ | ☐ | |
| | ☐ | ☐ | ☐ | ☐ | ☐ | |

| NAME | DAY GUEST | EVENING GUEST | SAVE THE DATE SENT | INVITE SENT | ATTENDING | GIFT |
|---|---|---|---|---|---|---|
| _____ | ☐ | ☐ | ☐ | ☐ | ☐ | _____ |
| _____ | ☐ | ☐ | ☐ | ☐ | ☐ | _____ |
| _____ | ☐ | ☐ | ☐ | ☐ | ☐ | _____ |
| _____ | ☐ | ☐ | ☐ | ☐ | ☐ | _____ |
| _____ | ☐ | ☐ | ☐ | ☐ | ☐ | _____ |
| _____ | ☐ | ☐ | ☐ | ☐ | ☐ | _____ |
| _____ | ☐ | ☐ | ☐ | ☐ | ☐ | _____ |
| _____ | ☐ | ☐ | ☐ | ☐ | ☐ | _____ |
| _____ | ☐ | ☐ | ☐ | ☐ | ☐ | _____ |
| _____ | ☐ | ☐ | ☐ | ☐ | ☐ | _____ |
| _____ | ☐ | ☐ | ☐ | ☐ | ☐ | _____ |
| _____ | ☐ | ☐ | ☐ | ☐ | ☐ | _____ |
| _____ | ☐ | ☐ | ☐ | ☐ | ☐ | _____ |
| _____ | ☐ | ☐ | ☐ | ☐ | ☐ | _____ |
| _____ | ☐ | ☐ | ☐ | ☐ | ☐ | _____ |
| _____ | ☐ | ☐ | ☐ | ☐ | ☐ | _____ |
| _____ | ☐ | ☐ | ☐ | ☐ | ☐ | _____ |
| _____ | ☐ | ☐ | ☐ | ☐ | ☐ | _____ |
| _____ | ☐ | ☐ | ☐ | ☐ | ☐ | _____ |
| _____ | ☐ | ☐ | ☐ | ☐ | ☐ | _____ |
| _____ | ☐ | ☐ | ☐ | ☐ | ☐ | _____ |
| _____ | ☐ | ☐ | ☐ | ☐ | ☐ | _____ |
| _____ | ☐ | ☐ | ☐ | ☐ | ☐ | _____ |
| _____ | ☐ | ☐ | ☐ | ☐ | ☐ | _____ |
| _____ | ☐ | ☐ | ☐ | ☐ | ☐ | _____ |
| _____ | ☐ | ☐ | ☐ | ☐ | ☐ | _____ |
| _____ | ☐ | ☐ | ☐ | ☐ | ☐ | _____ |
| _____ | ☐ | ☐ | ☐ | ☐ | ☐ | _____ |
| _____ | ☐ | ☐ | ☐ | ☐ | ☐ | _____ |
| _____ | ☐ | ☐ | ☐ | ☐ | ☐ | _____ |
| _____ | ☐ | ☐ | ☐ | ☐ | ☐ | _____ |
| _____ | ☐ | ☐ | ☐ | ☐ | ☐ | _____ |
| _____ | ☐ | ☐ | ☐ | ☐ | ☐ | _____ |
| _____ | ☐ | ☐ | ☐ | ☐ | ☐ | _____ |
| _____ | ☐ | ☐ | ☐ | ☐ | ☐ | _____ |
| _____ | ☐ | ☐ | ☐ | ☐ | ☐ | _____ |
| _____ | ☐ | ☐ | ☐ | ☐ | ☐ | _____ |

| NAME | DAY GUEST | EVENING GUEST | SAVE THE DATE SENT | INVITE SENT | ATTENDING | GIFT |
|---|---|---|---|---|---|---|
| _____ | ☐ | ☐ | ☐ | ☐ | ☐ | _____ |
| _____ | ☐ | ☐ | ☐ | ☐ | ☐ | _____ |
| _____ | ☐ | ☐ | ☐ | ☐ | ☐ | _____ |
| _____ | ☐ | ☐ | ☐ | ☐ | ☐ | _____ |
| _____ | ☐ | ☐ | ☐ | ☐ | ☐ | _____ |
| _____ | ☐ | ☐ | ☐ | ☐ | ☐ | _____ |
| _____ | ☐ | ☐ | ☐ | ☐ | ☐ | _____ |
| _____ | ☐ | ☐ | ☐ | ☐ | ☐ | _____ |
| _____ | ☐ | ☐ | ☐ | ☐ | ☐ | _____ |
| _____ | ☐ | ☐ | ☐ | ☐ | ☐ | _____ |
| _____ | ☐ | ☐ | ☐ | ☐ | ☐ | _____ |
| _____ | ☐ | ☐ | ☐ | ☐ | ☐ | _____ |
| _____ | ☐ | ☐ | ☐ | ☐ | ☐ | _____ |
| _____ | ☐ | ☐ | ☐ | ☐ | ☐ | _____ |
| _____ | ☐ | ☐ | ☐ | ☐ | ☐ | _____ |
| _____ | ☐ | ☐ | ☐ | ☐ | ☐ | _____ |
| _____ | ☐ | ☐ | ☐ | ☐ | ☐ | _____ |
| _____ | ☐ | ☐ | ☐ | ☐ | ☐ | _____ |
| _____ | ☐ | ☐ | ☐ | ☐ | ☐ | _____ |
| _____ | ☐ | ☐ | ☐ | ☐ | ☐ | _____ |
| _____ | ☐ | ☐ | ☐ | ☐ | ☐ | _____ |
| _____ | ☐ | ☐ | ☐ | ☐ | ☐ | _____ |
| _____ | ☐ | ☐ | ☐ | ☐ | ☐ | _____ |
| _____ | ☐ | ☐ | ☐ | ☐ | ☐ | _____ |
| _____ | ☐ | ☐ | ☐ | ☐ | ☐ | _____ |
| _____ | ☐ | ☐ | ☐ | ☐ | ☐ | _____ |
| _____ | ☐ | ☐ | ☐ | ☐ | ☐ | _____ |
| _____ | ☐ | ☐ | ☐ | ☐ | ☐ | _____ |
| _____ | ☐ | ☐ | ☐ | ☐ | ☐ | _____ |
| _____ | ☐ | ☐ | ☐ | ☐ | ☐ | _____ |
| _____ | ☐ | ☐ | ☐ | ☐ | ☐ | _____ |
| _____ | ☐ | ☐ | ☐ | ☐ | ☐ | _____ |
| _____ | ☐ | ☐ | ☐ | ☐ | ☐ | _____ |
| _____ | ☐ | ☐ | ☐ | ☐ | ☐ | _____ |
| _____ | ☐ | ☐ | ☐ | ☐ | ☐ | _____ |
| _____ | ☐ | ☐ | ☐ | ☐ | ☐ | _____ |
| _____ | ☐ | ☐ | ☐ | ☐ | ☐ | _____ |

# SEATING PLANS

Tradition plays a major part in where people sit on your wedding day. Arranging your family and friends at the reception can be tricky, that's why we suggest using an online planner for help and support. You may want to use the planner overleaf as a rough guide.

## THE HEAD TABLE
## (BRIDE & GROOM'S TABLE)

As Mr & Mrs you may want to sit on a rectangular table at the end of the room, some venues will raise this higher off of the ground to create a focal point.

It's tradition that the groom sits to the bride's right and the best man sits to her left. The maid of honor typically sits to the groom's right, although it's completely up to you to do things your way.

## TYPICAL HEAD TABLE LAYOUTS

Families can sometimes be complicated and depending on your own family arrangements setup this may change. Remember, there is no 'right and wrong'. Do what makes you feel comfortable, it's your wedding and your day!

**Traditional Seating Plan**

| GROOM'S MOTHER | BRIDE'S FATHER | MAID OF HONOR | GROOM ↓ | BRIDE ↓ | BEST MAN | BRIDE'S MOTHER | GROOM'S FATHER |
|---|---|---|---|---|---|---|---|

**Popular Alternative Plan**

| MAID OF HONOR | GROOM'S FATHER | BRIDE'S MOTHER | GROOM ↓ | BRIDE ↓ | BRIDE'S FATHER | GROOM'S MOTHER | BEST MAN |
|---|---|---|---|---|---|---|---|

# HEAD TABLE

TABLE NAME / NUMBER

1
2
3
4
5
6
7
8
9
10
11
12

TABLE NAME / NUMBER

1
2
3
4
5
6
7
8
9
10
11
12

TABLE NAME / NUMBER

1
2
3
4
5
6
7
8
9
10
11
12

TABLE NAME
/ NUMBER:

1
2
3
4
5
6
7
8
9
10
11
12

TABLE NAME
/ NUMBER:

1
2
3
4
5
6
7
8
9
10
11
12

TABLE NAME
/ NUMBER:

1
2
3
4
5
6
7
8
9
10
11
12

TABLE NAME
/ NUMBER:

1
2
3
4
5
6
7
8
9
10
11
12

TABLE NAME
/ NUMBER:

1
2
3
4
5
6
7
8
9
10
11
12

TABLE NAME
/ NUMBER:

1
2
3
4
5
6
7
8
9
10
11
12

TABLE NAME / NUMBER:

1
2
3
4
5
6
7
8
9
10
11
12

TABLE NAME / NUMBER:

1
2
3
4
5
6
7
8
9
10
11
12

TABLE NAME / NUMBER:

1
2
3
4
5
6
7
8
9
10
11
12

TABLE NAME / NUMBER:

1
2
3
4
5
6
7
8
9
10
11
12

TABLE NAME / NUMBER:

1
2
3
4
5
6
7
8
9
10
11
12

TABLE NAME / NUMBER:

1
2
3
4
5
6
7
8
9
10
11
12

TABLE NAME
/ NUMBER:

1
2
3
4
5
6
7
8
9
10
11
12

TABLE NAME
/ NUMBER:

1
2
3
4
5
6
7
8
9
10
11
12

TABLE NAME
/ NUMBER:

1
2
3
4
5
6
7
8
9
10
11
12

TABLE NAME
/ NUMBER:

1
2
3
4
5
6
7
8
9
10
11
12

TABLE NAME
/ NUMBER:

1
2
3
4
5
6
7
8
9
10
11
12

TABLE NAME
/ NUMBER:

1
2
3
4
5
6
7
8
9
10
11
12

# TABLE LAYOUTS

Use this space to add tables & decide where your guests will sit

# TABLE LAYOUTS

Use this space to add tables & decide where your guests will sit

# YOUR GIFT LIST

Putting together your gift list is one of the best parts of planning your wedding. You have spent months deciding on how to treat your guests, now it's time for your guests to treat you.

You should discuss this with your partner and talk about what both of your wishes are.

**Useful points to discuss:-**

- Do you want physical gifts or financial gifts? Or both?

- Do you want to give anything to charity?

- What are your plans after the wedding? Moving home? Traveling?

- Do you need anything new to furnish your new home?

- Do you want people to pay for or buy experiences on your honeymoon?

There are lots of great gift list websites that you can use to help you with this process.

## NOTE:

We've also created an online gift list template that you can download that may help you further.

# YOUR GIFT LIST

| ITEM | WHERE FROM | QUANTITY | PRICE |
|------|-----------|----------|-------|
| Example: LUX Champagne Flutes | Macy's | 8 | $80 |

| ITEM | WHERE FROM | QUANTITY | PRICE |
|---|---|---|---|
| Example: LUX Champagne Flues | Macy's | 8 | $80 |
|  |  |  |  |
|  |  |  |  |
|  |  |  |  |
|  |  |  |  |
|  |  |  |  |
|  |  |  |  |
|  |  |  |  |
|  |  |  |  |
|  |  |  |  |
|  |  |  |  |
|  |  |  |  |
|  |  |  |  |
|  |  |  |  |
|  |  |  |  |
|  |  |  |  |
|  |  |  |  |
|  |  |  |  |
|  |  |  |  |
|  |  |  |  |
|  |  |  |  |
|  |  |  |  |
|  |  |  |  |
|  |  |  |  |
|  |  |  |  |
|  |  |  |  |
|  |  |  |  |
|  |  |  |  |
|  |  |  |  |
|  |  |  |  |
|  |  |  |  |
|  |  |  |  |
|  |  |  |  |
|  |  |  |  |
|  |  |  |  |
|  |  |  |  |
|  |  |  |  |
|  |  |  |  |
|  |  |  |  |
|  |  |  |  |
|  |  |  |  |
|  |  |  |  |
|  |  |  |  |
|  |  |  |  |
|  |  |  |  |
|  |  |  |  |
|  |  |  |  |
|  |  |  |  |
|  |  |  |  |
|  |  |  |  |
|  |  |  |  |

| ITEM | WHERE FROM | QUANTITY | PRICE |
|------|-----------|----------|-------|
| Example: LUX Champagne Flues | Macy's | 8 | $80 |

# NOTES

# NOTES

# NOTES

# NOTES

# NOTES

# CHOOSING YOUR WEDDING VENUE

Choosing your wedding venue is no doubt one of the biggest decisions you will have to make. It will set the tone for your whole wedding day. Depending on your priorities for the day it's likely going to be the single highest individual cost, so make sure you and your partner are both in agreement before putting down a deposit.

Make sure to visit at least a few wedding venues before making your decision. Many venues offer varying packages, costs and facilities.

## REMEMBER

**LOCATION:** Consider the location of your venue. Will your guests be able to get there easily? Is it near to any airports?

**CAPACITY:** How many guests can the venue hold? Can you fit everyone in? Is there enough room in the evening for all of your evening guests?

**BUDGET:** What are the costs for each guest? Are there room rental fees? Costs for evening guests? Is catering included? What about setup and breakdown fees?

**STYLE:** Does the décor suit your wedding theme? Are you allowed to decorate the venue?

**GUEST ACCOMMODATION:** Is there accommodation for guests? If not, where will guests coming from out of town stay? Are there local hotels? Motels? AirBnb?

**THE STAFF:** Did the people that are going to be running your day seem professional? Do they care?

# VENUE SHORTLIST

**1**

Venue Name
Contact Name

Capacity

Contact Number
Email
Allow Kids?
Restrictions
Accommodation
Notes

Dates Available

Day          Evening

**2**

Venue Name
Contact Name

Capacity

Contact Number
Email
Allow Kids?
Restrictions
Accommodation
Notes

Dates Available

Day          Evening

## MONEY SAVING TIP:

Mid week weddings are a great way of saving money, with prices up to half of what you would normally pay in peak season. Ask your venue about any offers & promotions!

**3**

Venue Name

Contact Name

Dates Available

Day                    Evening

Capacity

Contact Number

Email

Allow Kids?

Restrictions

Accommodation

Notes

**4**

Venue Name

Contact Name

Dates Available

Day                    Evening

Capacity

Contact Number

Email

Allow Kids?

Restrictions

Accommodation

Notes

**5**

Venue Name

Contact Name

Dates Available

Day                    Evening

Capacity

Contact Number

Email

Allow Kids?

Restrictions

Accommodation

Notes

**6**

Venue Name

Contact Name

Capacity · Day · Evening

Dates Available

Contact Number

Email

Allow Kids?

Restrictions

Accommodation

Notes

**7**

Venue Name

Contact Name

Capacity · Day · Evening

Dates Available

Contact Number

Email

Allow Kids?

Restrictions

Accommodation

Notes

## TIP:

Many wedding venues will offer discounted room rates for wedding guests, they may even offer a complimentary stay in the Bridal Suite for you too.

Always negotiate, the more savings you can make, the more money you have to spend on other parts of your day.

# GUEST ACCOMMODATION

**\* If you are getting married at a hotel or venue with guest accommodation you can miss this section. \***

Depending on where you are getting married, you may want to arrange accommodation for your guests. Remember, people will come from far and wide, so find a range of accommodation for different needs.

## MONEY SAVING TIP:

You can group book rooms with a hotel and you may find that your chosen hotel can give you a group booking discount.

Don't feel obligated to pay for all of the rooms. People are often happy to cover the cost of their room at a wedding.

## ACCOMMODATION OPTIONS

| 1 | | Notes |
|---|---|---|
| Accommodation Name | | |
| Distance To Venue | | |
| No. Rooms Available | | |
| No. Family Rooms Available | | |
| Cost Per Room | | |
| Is Breakfast Included? | | |

**2**

Accommodation Name

Distance To Venue

No. Rooms Available

No. Family Rooms Available

Cost Per Room

Is Breakfast Included?

Notes

**3**

Accommodation Name

Distance To Venue

No. Rooms Available

No. Family Rooms Available

Cost Per Room

Is Breakfast Included?

Notes

**4**

Accommodation Name

Distance To Venue

No. Rooms Available

No. Family Rooms Available

Cost Per Room

Is Breakfast Included?

Notes

# CHOOSING YOUR VENDORS

Choosing your wedding vendors is such an exciting part of the planning process. Your vendors will help determine the feel and flow of the day.

It's worth contacting your vendors as early as possible, as the best ones often get booked up early.

## REMEMBER

**Budget:** Don't go over budget, stick to what you know you can afford. Make sure you are open with your budget. Ask them not to show you things outside of your budget to avoid disappointment...

**Location:** Always consider the location of your wedding when choosing vendors. Will your preferred vendor want to travel to you? Are there additional costs / savings that can be made?

**Style:** Do your vendors match the style of your wedding? Do they fully understand your vision?

## TIP:

Typically a Bride / Groom will contact vendors after they've selected their venue and wedding date.

# CHOOSING YOUR WEDDING PHOTOGRAPHER/VIDEOGRAPHER

Choosing your photographer and videographer is so important, for most couples it will be the lasting memory from your special day. When planning your day, discuss with your partner how much time you want to spend taking photos and how important having photos with everyone is to you both. For some people just having photos with immediate family and some couple shots are plenty.

If you already have your heart set on a photographer why not ask them for their recommendations on a suitable videographer – or vice versa. It's likely that they will know of another vendor that has a similar style to match.

## TIP:

Choose a photographer that has a portfolio that reflects your style and matches how you would like your wedding to be remembered. Do you want a simple record of the main parts of your day? Do you want those little touches and memories captured? What about capturing the emotion? The pre-wedding build up?

|  | Photographer | Videographer |
|---|---|---|
| Name |  |  |
| Website |  |  |
| Price |  |  |
| Engagement Shoot? |  |  |
| On The Day |  |  |
| Wedding Album / DVD / USB? |  |  |

## MONEY SAVING TIP:

Try to pick a photographer based on the style of photos that you want (rather than just based on price). If price is an issue, you can always opt to get the photographs taken and a wedding album made at a later time!

# QUESTIONS FOR THE PHOTOGRAPHER...

- Is my wedding date available?
- What is your preferred photography style?
- Have you ever photographed a wedding at my venue before?
- Will you be the one photographing my wedding?
- Are there any others in your team?
- What if there is an emergency and you can't photograph my wedding?
- Can I see the full album from a wedding?
- What do your packages include?
- How and when will I receive my proofs?

- How many photographers will cover my wedding?
- Will you have a second shooter or assistant?
- How long have you been photographing weddings and how many weddings do you photograph a year?
- How do you like to schedule a wedding day?
- Can I see a copy of your contract?
- What hours are included?
- Do you charge for overtime?
- Are you insured?
- Can you recommend a videographer?

## TIP:

Check the 'Our Wedding Day' section for tips on creating the photographer's check list.

## NOTES

# QUESTIONS FOR THE VIDEOGRAPHER...

- Is my wedding date available?
- What is your preferred videography style?
- Have you ever filmed a wedding at my venue before?
- Will you be the one filming my wedding?
- Are there any others in your team?
- What if there is an emergency and you can't attend my wedding?
- Can I see a video or watch a trailer from a recent wedding?
- What do your packages include?
- How and when will I receive my trailer and final edit?

- How many videographers will cover my wedding?
- Will you have a second shooter or assistant?
- How long have you been filming weddings and how many weddings do you carry out a year?
- How do you like to schedule a wedding day?
- Can I see a copy of your contract?
- What hours are included?
- Do you charge for overtime?
- Are you insured?
- Can you recommend a photographer?

## NOTES

# THE DRESS

They say you **just know** when you've found your perfect dress... but it's ok if you don't find it straight away. Visit at least two or three bridal boutiques and try on as many different designs and styles as possible. The consultants in dress stores are usually very knowledgeable and want to help you find your perfect dress within your budget.

You may have a style in mind that you like before trying dresses on, but make sure you also try on different dress styles. You only get to do this once, and dresses that you think may not suit you may just surprise you.

## THINGS TO ASK

- Do you offer alterations in store?
- How many appointments do you recommend?
- I am planning to lose / gain weight before the wedding. How will this affect the dress I've chosen?
- Can I take any photos?
- What is included in the price?
- How many people can I bring with me when I try dresses on?

- What dress styles would look best for my body shape?
- Can I try a veil with this? What options are available?
- Are alterations included in the price?
- What shoes / underwear / accessories do you recommend with my dress?
- Will the dress be steamed when I come to pick it up?

## MY FAVORITE DRESSES

# BRIDESMAID'S DRESSES

Choosing your bridesmaid's dresses is something that you should do with at least one of your bridesmaids.

Do some research on your own first so that you understand what styles you like, and then discuss this with your bridesmaids.

Bridesmaid's dresses should complement your dress but not be comparable to it.

Whilst the bridesmaids should look a million dollars, remember the focus of the big day is on you; your bridesmaids should complement but not upstage you.

| Bridesmaid Name | Dress Size | Color / Design |
|---|---|---|
| | | |
| | | |
| | | |
| | | |
| | | |
| | | |
| | | |

**1**
Store / Designer
Dress Name
Color
Price

Notes

**2**
Store / Designer
Dress Name
Color
Price

Notes

# GROOM'S OUTFIT

Ask the groom to get measured up for his wedding suit / tux a few months before the wedding

| | | Notes |
|---|---|---|
| Store / Designer | | |
| Suit Name / Model No. | | |
| Color | | |
| Price | | |
| Jacket Size | | |
| Collar Size | | |
| Waist Size | | |
| Leg Size | | |
| Shoe Size | | |

# GROOMSMAN OUTFITS

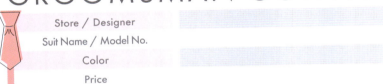

| | | Notes |
|---|---|---|
| Store / Designer | | |
| Suit Name / Model No. | | |
| Color | | |
| Price | | |

| Groomsman Name | Jacket Size | Collar Size | Waist Size | Leg Length | Shoe Size | Additional Notes |
|---|---|---|---|---|---|---|
| | | | | | | |
| | | | | | | |
| | | | | | | |
| | | | | | | |
| | | | | | | |
| | | | | | | |
| | | | | | | |
| | | | | | | |
| | | | | | | |

# CATERERS

Your wedding caterer is one of the most important vendors for your entire day.

As well as preparing your wedding menu they will help to coordinate your wedding reception and the flow of the day.

Most caterers can supply all of the rentals too like silverware, plates and chairs and some will offer to make the cake too.

We recommend all brides to be up-front about your budget straight away. Ask your caterer what options are available to you to work around your budget.

Before you book, ensure that you try to ask as many of these questions as possible.

## QUESTIONS TO ASK THE CATERER

- Is my wedding date available?
- Which catering style do you offer? Plated Dinner, Buffet, Family or Cocktail style?
- Is the menu fixed choices?
- What is and isn't included in your pricing?
- How many waitstaff / servers will there be?
- How many weddings do you do per year?
- What about rentals? Silverware, plates, napkins, chairs etc.

- Do you provide tablecloths?
- Do you offer wine and beer?
- Do you have a liquor licence? Do you have liquor insurance?
- Have you got other weddings on the same day as my wedding?
- What are your specialty dishes?
- How many dishes can we try at our food tasting?

# MORE QUESTIONS TO ASK THE CATERER

- Do you cater to all dietary requirements? (Allergies, Gluten Free, Vegan)
- What are the prices per head?
- Have you got any references from past clients?
- Can you make my wedding cake?
- Is there a setup and breakdown fee?
- Is cleaning included?
- When do you require the final menu choices?
- What about meals for kids / infants?

- Do you provide vendor meals?
- Do you have any references from former clients?
- What do the waitstaff wear? Does it complement your color scheme?
- Do you place the namecards on each table?
- What fees are additional? Taxes, Service Fees, Tipping, Security Deposit
- Can you offer any speciality cocktails?
- Can you supply a cake knife / cake stand?

# MY CATERER

| | | |
|---|---|---|
| Vendor Name | Contact Name | |
| Email | Tel | |

| | | Notes |
|---|---|---|
| Canapés | | |
| Starter | | |
| Main Course | | |
| Dessert | | |
| Price Per Head (Day) | | |
| Price Per Head (Evening) | | |
| Total | | |

# FLORIST / FLORAL DESIGNER

Your wedding flowers will help transform your wedding venue and will bring together your color scheme and style perfectly.

We recommend speaking to florist(s) around 9 months before your wedding, once you have your venue chosen and know what areas will require flowers.

## QUESTIONS TO ASK YOUR FLORIST

❀ Is my wedding date available?

❀ My theme is
Can you recommend flowers to complement my theme?

❀ Do you offer a design service?

❀ Are there setup and breakdown charges?

❀ What is your style? Modern, Minimalist, Extravagant?

❀ What flowers are in season at the time of my wedding?

❀ Do you have any other weddings on the day of my wedding?

❀ Will you be at my wedding? Or a member of your team?

❀ Have you worked at my venue before? Can I see any photos?

❀ What about rentals? Candelabras etc.

❀ What about a chuppah or garland?

❀ Do we need flowers for the aisles?

❀ Can we re-use the ceremony flowers at the reception?

| Vendor Name | | Contact Name | |
|---|---|---|---|
| Email | | Phone Number | |
| Notes | | | |

## TIP:

Don't forget to show your florist your Vision Boards.

# WEDDING CAKE

**\* Some caterers will be able to make your wedding cake.
If you want something specialist find a specialist cake baker \***

Before choosing your cake baker and setting up a tasting session make sure you ask these questions...

 Can you make the cake for my wedding day?

 Can you match my theme / color scheme?

 I have       guests. How big should my cake be?

 What are the flavor choices?

 What are the filling choices?

 Can you make sugar flowers?

 Can you deliver?

 What about a cake knife?

 Is there a setup or breakdown charge?

 How far in advance do I need to book?

 How many days before my wedding will you make the cake? Will it be fresh?

 Are you making my cake? Or one of your team?

 Do you offer cake stands? Is there a rental fee?

 Do you have a licence?

 How are your cakes priced?

 Do you offer vegan / gluten free options?

 Do you offer a tasting consultation?

 Do you use buttercream or fondant?

 Can you work with fresh flowers?

# WEDDING CAKE VENDOR

| | |
|---|---|
| **Vendor Name** | **Contact Name** |
| Email | Phone Number |
| Style | Notes |
| No. Guests (Size) | |
| Flavor(s) | |
| Filling | |
| Extras | |
| **Price Agreed** | |

# WEDDING HAIR

Remember to show your vision boards or any photos to your hair stylist to give them inspiration and help them to understand your vision.

## THINGS TO ASK

- Do you have my date available?
- Have they got any other weddings booked on the same day?
- Does the hair stylist have a portfolio?
- Do I need to supply any tools or hair products?
- How do you charge? Hourly? Fixed rate? Per person?
- Can you travel to my venue or do I need to travel to you?
- Can I do a pre-wedding hair trial?
- What happens if you are not able to attend my wedding day? Illness etc.
- Do you have any assistants?
- How long will it take for me and for my bridesmaids?
- What time do we need to start if my arrival is scheduled for         :         ?

## THINGS TO CONSIDER

- Do all of your bridesmaids need their hair professionally styled?
- Can any of your bridesmaids do their own?

## HAIR STYLIST

Hair Stylist Name

Phone Number

Email

Bride's Hair

Bridesmaids' Hair

Flower Girls' Hair

Price Agreed

# WEDDING MAKE-UP

Remember to show your vision boards or any photos to your make up artist to give them inspiration and help them to understand your vision.

## THINGS TO ASK

- Do you have my date available?
- Have they got any other weddings booked on the same day?
- Does the make-up artist have a portfolio?
- How do you charge? Hourly? Fixed rate? Per person?
- Can you travel to my venue or do I need to travel to you?
- Will you be doing any other weddings on the day of my wedding?
- Can I do a pre-wedding make up trial?
- What happens if you are not able to attend my wedding day? Illness etc.
- Do you have any assistants?
- How long will it take for me and for my bridesmaids?
- What time do we need to arrive if my wedding is at         :        ?

## THINGS TO CONSIDER

- Do all of your bridesmaids need make-up?
- Can any of your bridesmaids do their own make-up?

## MAKE UP

Make Up Artist Name
Phone Number
Email
Bride's Make Up
Bridesmaids' Make Up
Price Agreed

# BEAUTY TREATMENTS

**Have you remembered to book all of your treatments?**

## MANICURE

Vendor

Phone Number

Name

Cost

Email

Date

Time

Notes

## PEDICURE

Vendor

Phone Number

Name

Cost

Email

Date

Time

Notes

# WAXING

Vendor

Name

Email

Date

| Phone Number | |
|---|---|
| Cost | |
| Time | |

Notes

# MASSAGE

Vendor

Name

Email

Date

| Phone Number | |
|---|---|
| Cost | |
| Time | |

Notes

# OTHER

Vendor

Name

Email

Date

| Phone Number | |
|---|---|
| Cost | |
| Time | |

Notes

# THE OFFICIANT

Wherever your wedding ceremony takes place, it is important to ensure that your wedding officiant is someone who you and your partner trust and respect to carry out your wedding.

If your nuptials will take place in a church or synagogue, you may not need to book an officiant (as there will already be one in residence).

Before your wedding it is good to get to know your officiant.

It will help them deliver a more intimate and personalized ceremony for you and your guests.

Whether you are having a civil ceremony, a religious ceremony or something in between, we've collated some great questions for you to ask any potential officiants.

## GOOD QUESTIONS TO ASK THE OFFICIANT

- Are you able to marry us at a non-religious venue?
- Do you perform ceremonies of inter-faith (may not be applicable)?
- Will you offer a sermon?
- Will you do a speech?
- Can we hear the speech beforehand?
- Is my photographer / videographer allowed in the church / synagogue?
- Can you support us with writing our vows?

- Can we have our own vows?
- Can we have our own readings?
- Can we have our own poems?
- What is the policy on music during the ceremony?
- Is there a ceremony fee or suggested donation?
- Are they available for a rehearsal?
- Do they have any sample readings from previous weddings?

## CHOSEN OFFICIANT

Name

Phone Number

Email

Address

# WEDDING TRANSPORT

## THINGS TO ASK

You'll want to travel to your wedding in style. Make sure you know what is and is not included with these handy hints and tips.

- 🚗 Do you have my date available?
- 🚗 Will you be doing any other weddings on the day of my wedding?
- 🚗 What wedding vehicles do you have available?
- 🚗 Is the groom allowed to drive the car away after the ceremony?
- 🚗 What about insurance?
- 🚗 What happens if the chauffeur turns up late? Or is not able to attend?
- 🚗 How does the pricing work? By time or distance?
- 🚗 Can we decorate the vehicle(s)?
- 🚗 How does tipping work?
- 🚗 What will the chauffeur be wearing?
- 🚗 Are there any extras available?
- 🚗 Are there any hidden costs?

## TRANSPORT COMPANY

Company Name

Phone Number

Email

Vehicle(s) Hired

Terms Agreed

Price Agreed

## NOTES

# ENTERTAINMENT

Whether it's a DJ, a live band, magician, live performers or even some food based entertainment... Your guests are waiting to be impressed, so show them a great time!

Entertainment will really enhance the atmosphere and inject fun and personality into your wedding.

For your evening guests this will be one of the main things that they remember about your big day.

Choose vendors that match your style, your personalities and that will make your wedding stand out from the rest.

### 1
Company Name

Phone Number

Email

Special Requirements

Notes

### 2
Company Name

Phone Number

Email

Special Requirements

Notes

### 3
Company Name

Phone Number

Email

Special Requirements

Notes

**4**
Company Name
Phone Number
Email
Special Requirements

Notes

**5**
Company Name
Phone Number
Email
Special Requirements

Notes

**6**
Company Name
Phone Number
Email
Special Requirements

Notes

**7**
Company Name
Phone Number
Email
Special Requirements

Notes

**8**
Company Name
Phone Number
Email
Special Requirements

Notes

# FAVORS

Favors can be a lovely gesture to thank your guests for coming to share your day with you both. Favors can also be a lovely keepsake from your day... unless of course they're edible!

Your wedding favors can be as low cost or expensive as you like. If you are working on a tight budget why not get your bridesmaids or groomsmen to help you with some handmade wedding favors?

## POPULAR IDEAS

- Home Made Liquor / Gin
- Home Brewed Beer / Wine
- Baked Cookies, Brownies or Sweet Treats
- Jams & Preserves
- Oils
- Candles

- Flowers & Seeds
- Lottery Tickets
- Coasters
- Playing Cards
- Soaps & Perfumes
- Artisan Coffee & Tea
- Mints

## NOTES

# WEDDING BANDS

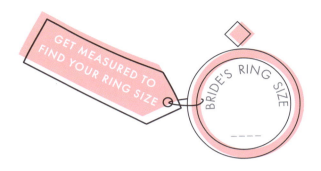

**GET MEASURED TO FIND YOUR RING SIZE**

BRIDE'S RING SIZE ____

GROOM'S RING SIZE ____

## TIPS ON CHOOSING YOUR RINGS

◆ Take with you any photos and ideas that you like to give your jeweler some inspiration.

◆ Set your budget.... Gold, Diamonds, Platinum and Silver are all precious materials... it's easy to get carried away and go over budget.

◆ Consider your job/career and your lifestyle - If you work a lot with your hands will your wedding ring get in the way?

◆ Buy both your rings together, you may be able to negotiate a discount.

◆ Don't worry about matching. It's completely normal for the bride & groom to have differing styles.

| Jewelry Store | | | |
|---|---|---|---|
| Bride's Ring Name | | | |
| Price | | | |
| Groom's Ring Name | | | |
| Price | | | |

## NOTES

# STATIONERY

You will want to get wedding stationery designed for your wedding. Choose a local graphic designer or stationer that can match your style.

| Item | Info | Quantity | Cost | Arrival Date |
|------|------|----------|------|--------------|
| Engagement Party Invites | | | | |
| Save The Date Cards | | | | |
| Bridal Shower Invites | | | | |
| Bachelor/Bachelorette Invitations | | | | |
| Wedding Invitations | | | | |
| Ceremony Programs | | | | |
| Place Cards / Escort Cards | | | | |
| Table Number Cards | | | | |
| Menu Cards | | | | |
| Favor Cards | | | | |
| Thank You Cards | | | | |
| | | | | |
| | | | | |
| | | | | |

**ADD IN MORE HERE**

## TIP:

There are additional notes pages at the end of this section if you need them.

## NOTES

# YOUR WEDDING WEBSITE

Whilst not essential, a wedding website can be a stress free way to keep everyone informed about what is happening on your wedding day.

**Useful info to have:**

- ♡ RSVP (with contact box for dietary requirements)
- ♡ About You / Your Partner
- ♡ Your Wedding Party
- ♡ Links To Guest Accommodation
- ♡ Venue Address and Timings
- ♡ Your Contact Info
- ♡ Link To Gift List
- ♡ Thank You (after wedding)
- ♡ Link To Wedding Video / Photos (after wedding)

**Remember:** Your website doesn't need to be a design masterpiece, it just needs to be informative.

## TIP:

Many of the major wedding websites allow you to create a free wedding website yourself. If you want something bespoke speak to a few local website designers.

## NOTES

# ADDITIONAL VENDOR INFO

### Add details of any additional vendors here

**1**

Vendor
Name

Contact
Name

Service

Phone
Number

Email

Notes

**2**

Vendor
Name

Contact
Name

Service

Phone
Number

Email

Notes

**3**

Vendor
Name

Contact
Name

Service

Phone
Number

Email

Notes

**4**

Vendor Name

Service

Email

Contact Name

Phone Number

Notes

**5**

Vendor Name

Service

Email

Contact Name

Phone Number

Notes

**6**

Vendor Name

Service

Email

Contact Name

Phone Number

Notes

**7**

Vendor Name

Service

Email

Contact Name

Phone Number

Notes

**8**

Vendor Name

Service

Email

Notes

Contact Name

Phone Number

---

**9**

Vendor Name

Service

Email

Notes

Contact Name

Phone Number

---

**10**

Vendor Name

Service

Email

Notes

Contact Name

Phone Number

# RESEARCHING HONEYMOON DESTINATIONS

Most couples go on honeymoon straight after their wedding, however you may find that some months are better than others depending on where you want to visit.

## TIP:

You can do your research online but make sure you speak to a travel consultant. Their knowledge of climates and destinations are invaluable as well as their contacts who may be able to get you some extras thrown in.

Remember: Whilst the Caribbean may sound like a tropical paradise, you don't want to be traveling in hurricane season!!

Assuming you want to head for the sun, here are some general weather rules. Always check with a travel consultant or online for more accurate weather information.

○ **Bahamas and Caribbean**
**Best times:** November to April

○ **Europe**
**Best times:** May to September

○ **Mauritius**
**Best times:** April to December

○ **Florida**
**Best times:** March, April, October and November

○ **Hawaii**
**Best times:** March to July, September to November

○ **Mexico**
**Best times:** November to May

○ **Maldives**
**Best times:** November to April

○ **Southeast Asia**
**Best times:** November to April

○ **South Pacific, French Polynesia**
**Best times:** May to October

# HONEYMOON NOTES

# NOTES

# NOTES

# NOTES

# TO DO

# TO DO

# TO DO

# READINGS

It's traditional (and compulsory for some religious ceremonies) to have a reading. Ask your officiant about the requirements for your wedding ceremony. There are hundreds of readings to choose from online to suit every style.

# WHO TO CHOOSE TO DO YOUR READINGS

- Make sure you choose confident speakers
- Make sure that whoever you choose is happy to do a reading
- Readings are a great way to honor people and make them feel a real part of your day

## OUR TOP BIBLICAL READINGS

**1 Corinthians** Chapter 13

**Genesis** Chapter 1, v26-28

**Ephesians** Chapter 5, v21-33

**Colossians** Chapter 3, v12-17

## OUR TOP NON-BIBLICAL READINGS

Love Is An Adventure
**Pierre Tielhart de Chardin**

Captain Corelli's Mandolin
**Louis de Bernières**

Jane Eyre
**Charlotte Brontë**

Untitled
**R.M Drake**

# OUR READINGS

Reading: _____

Read by: _____

Reading: _____

Read by: _____

Reading: _____

Read by: _____

Reading: _____

Read by: _____

# MUSIC CHOICES

This is definitely one of the most fun parts of planning your day. The music will set the mood for the day. Have a look online at playlists and use iTunes / Spotify to create playlists.

| | Song Title | Artist | Special Timings |
|---|---|---|---|
| Example | At Last | Etta James | Fade out at 1m: 12s |
| Ceremony Entrance Song | | | |
| Ceremony Exit Song | | | |
| Wedding Breakfast | | | |
| Entrance Song | | | |
| Evening Entrance Song (before first dance) | | | |
| First Dance Song | | | |
| End of Night Last Song | | | |
| | | | |
| | | | |
| | | | |

# REMEMBER

If you aren't having a DJ, you'll want to make an evening playlist. Choose crowd pleasing songs, to suit guests of all ages.

# CREATING YOUR PHOTOGRAPHY LIST

The photography list will make sure you get all of the right photos to help you remember your wedding. It's generally a good idea to assign this to one of the groomsmen who can work with the photographer on the day to get people organized.

From our experience getting all of the photos you need can be stressful. It's good to discuss this with your photographer before the wedding, to ensure your expectations are met.

## Pre Wedding Ceremony

- Shot of wedding invitation
- Bride / Bridesmaid's hair and make up
- Dress hanging, jewelry laid out, shoes etc.
- Bouquets and buttonholes /corsages
- Bride putting on dress
- Bridal party having fun
- Close up of dress details
- Putting on jewelry & shoes
- Close up of Bride holding bouquet
- Mother / Father and Bride portrait
- Family shots
- Wedding ring shots
- Bride spending moment alone
- Bridal party walking down stairs / leaving the house
- Bride and Father in wedding car
- Groom and Groomsmen getting ready
- Groom spending moment alone

## The Journey To The Ceremony

- Bride and Father / Mother
- Bride and Bridesmaids / Flowergirls
- Groom and Groomsmen /Pageboys

## Informal Shots

- Shots with friends
- Bride showing her new ring to the guests
- Shots of guests eating, drinking, and chatting

## Your Ceremony

- Venue being decorated
- Groom and Groomsmen outside
- Guests outside and inside church
- Groomsmen handing out programs
- Bride arriving / getting out of the wedding car
- Bridal party entrance
- Newlywed shot

- Bride walking up the aisle
- Bride being given away
- Exchanging of vows
- Lighting of unity candle
- Ring bearer
- Exchanging of the rings
- The first kiss as husband and wife
- Signing the register
- Walking back down the aisle

- Confetti throwing
- Greeting guests outside venue
- Bride & Groom in the back seat of the wedding car
- Couple shots
- Portraits of the couple alone
- Portraits of Bride on her own
- Portraits of Groom on his own

## Bridal Party

- Bride and Groom with Bridesmaids /Groomsmen
- Entire bridal party

- Bride with Bridesmaids / Maid of Honor

- Groom and Groomsmen / Bestman

## Family

- Bride and Groom with her parents
- Bride and Groom with his parents

- Bride and Groom with both sets of parents
- Bride and Groom with siblings

- Bride and Groom with close family members

## Wedding Day - Reception

- The reception space set up - before room fills up
- Details and room décor shots - table settings, place cards, favors, candy buffet, centrepieces etc.
- Wedding cake detail shots

- Bride & Groom arriving
- Toasts and speeches
- Cutting the cake
- The first dance
- Bride dancing with Father / Groom dancing with Mother

- Bride and Groom mingling with guests
- Guests dancing
- Musicians, singers, DJ

# SAMPLE ITINERARY

| DESCRIPTION | TIME | OWNER |
|---|---|---|
| Photographer arrives | 09:05 | Lucy |
| Reception | | |
| Set Alarm & Wake Up! | | |
| Have Breakfast | | |
| Get Hair & Make Up Done | | |
| Get Dressed | | |
| Photographer & Videographer Arrives | | |
| Pictures of Bride | | |
| Pictures of Groom | | |
| Flowers Delivered to Church | | |
| Groom To Depart for Ceremony | | |
| Wedding Transport Arrives | | |
| Groomsmen to arrive at ceremony venue | | |
| Parents arrive at ceremony venue | | |
| Greet Guests and usher to seats | | |
| Groom Arrives & Welcomes Guests | | |
| Best Men To Carry Out Duties | | |
| Bride Arrives | | |
| Photos of Bride arriving | | |
| Ceremony Begins | | |
| Ceremony Ends | | |
| Photos | | |
| Bridal Party Photos at ceremony venue | | |
| Additional photos with bridal party at another venue | | |
| DJ / Musicians Arrive | | |
| Drive to reception venue | | |
| Drinks Reception | | |
| Guests all seated at Venue | | |
| Bride & Groom Entrance | | |
| Dinner or Evening Buffet Served | | |
| Cutting of the Cake | | |
| Toasts | | |
| Speeches | | |
| Your First Dance | | |
| Father / Daughter Dance | | |
| Mother / Son Dance | | |
| Garter / Bouquet Toss | | |
| The Final Song | | |
| Time To Leave The Reception | | |

# OUR ITINERARY

| DESCRIPTION | TIME | OWNER |
|---|---|---|
| | | |
| | | |
| | | |
| | | |
| | | |
| | | |
| | | |
| | | |
| | | |
| | | |
| | | |
| | | |
| | | |
| | | |
| | | |
| | | |
| | | |
| | | |
| | | |
| | | |
| | | |
| | | |
| | | |
| | | |
| | | |
| | | |
| | | |
| | | |
| | | |
| | | |
| | | |
| | | |
| | | |
| | | |

# OUR ITINERARY

| DESCRIPTION | TIME | OWNER |
|---|---|---|
| | | |

# WEDDING DAY SURVIVAL KIT

A week before your wedding ensure you pack a Wedding Day Survival Kit. Assign it to a member of your wedding party to look after. You never know when it may come in handy.

- Tissues
- Safety Pins
- Waterproof Mascara
- Bandaids
- Mints / Chewing Gum
- Deodorant
- Perfume
- Feet Gel Pads
- Flat Shoes (For Dancing)
- Hair Pins
- Lip Gloss / Lipstick / Lip Balm
- Nail File / Buffer
- Cotton Swabs

- Sewing Kit
- Chalk / Talcum Powder (in case of stains on your dress)
- Small Hair Brush
- Tampons / Sanitary pads
- Compact Mirror
- Face Wipes
- Tweezers
- False Nail Glue
- Scissors
- Spare Tights
- Concealer
- Any Medication

# HONEYMOON PACKING CHECKLIST

## MUST-HAVES

- ☐ Tickets
- ☐ Passports / Visas / Drivers Licence
- ☐ Currency & Credit Cards
- ☐ Booking Confirmations (Hotels, Restaurants, Excursions)
- ☐ Travel Insurance & Documents
- ☐ Medication
- ☐ Luggage Tags
- ☐ Camera

## BRIDE

- ☐ Jeans, Leggings
- ☐ Jacket, Jumpers and Cardigans
- ☐ Casual Dresses
- ☐ Smart Dresses
- ☐ Casual Tops & T Shirts
- ☐ Shorts
- ☐ Swimsuits & Bikinis
- ☐ Sneakers / Walking Boots
- ☐ Evening Footwear
- ☐ Day Footwear
- ☐ Purse & Clutch Bags
- ☐ Socks, Bras & Underwear
- ☐ Hats & Accessories
- ☐ Sunglasses
- ☐ Toiletries

## GROOM

- ☐ Jeans & Trousers
- ☐ Shorts & Swimming Shorts
- ☐ Casual Shirts, Polo Shirts & T Shirts
- ☐ Formal Shirts / Evening Jacket / Tux
- ☐ Evening Shoes & Boat Shoes
- ☐ Day Footwear – Flip Flops & Sandals
- ☐ Sneakers / Walking Shoes
- ☐ Socks & Underwear
- ☐ Hats & Accessories
- ☐ Sunglasses
- ☐ Toiletries

## SHARED

- ☐ Insect Repellent
- ☐ Sunscreen / Lip Balm / After Sun
- ☐ Small Medical Kit
- ☐ Books / Tablet
- ☐ Phone Chargers
- ☐ Cards / Games
- ☐ Travel Adaptor(s)
- ☐ Shampoo / Conditioners
- ☐ Antibacterial Gel / Wipes
- ☐ Small Backpack(s)

## LEAVE BEHIND WITH FAMILY OR FRIENDS

- ☐ Your Travel Details
- ☐ Itinerary Information

# WRITING YOUR VOWS

If you and your partner decide that you want to write your own vows you should try to do this at least a month before your wedding day. Many couples find it very difficult to express their feelings especially when it comes to putting pen to paper.

## THINGS TO CONSIDER

**Decide on the tone...** Are you going for humor? Are you aiming for romance? Are you going to share your vows with one another before the wedding or reveal them together on the day?

**Make some promises...** Your vows should include promises to one another. "I promise to always..."

**Try to be unique...** The classic 'cliché' vows have been used for generations. Show your personality and create something from the heart in your own style.

**Get inspired...** there are hundreds of blogs and great resources online with inspirational vows that you can adjust and personalize.

**Practise makes perfect...** Avoid suffering stage fright by practicing your vows over and over. Practise to a friend or family member, even in the shower or in front of the mirror.

**Write down notes on your relationship...** What is your strongest bond? When has your partner been there for you when you needed it? What about them inspires you? What do you love about them over everyone else?

**Aim for crowd pleasers...** You want your vows to be timeless, something that doesn't show age. Try to avoid inside jokes, code words or anecdotes, instead aim for something that you could happily read out to one another again in 30 years' time.

**Start early to avoid writer's block...** Give yourself at least a month before your wedding to avoid a last minute rush.

## TIP:

You'll want to print out your vows and take them with you on your wedding day. Use the pages overleaf to write draft vows, but remember to take a hard copy with you on your wedding day.

# WRITING YOUR VOWS

## YOUR VOWS

# WRITING YOUR VOWS

## YOUR PARTNERS' VOWS

# LAST MINUTE TO DO'S

# LAST MINUTE TO DO'S

# LAST MINUTE TO DO'S

# READY, STEADY, WED!

So your big day is finally here. Here are some handy last minute tips that we've compiled.

## TOP TIPS FOR YOUR BIG DAY...

- Go to bed early – sleep will keep you looking beautiful, rested and feeling refreshed!

- Have a good breakfast high in protein to keep you full for the morning

- Wake up early so you can relax when getting ready

- When getting hair and make up done, wear a dress shirt or robe gown to avoid pulling anything over your head

- Remember to take some time out together during the day

- Remember Your Wedding Day Survival Kit

- Leave your cell phone at home or with a friend / bridesmaid

- Try and say hello to everyone...

- Try to visit each table between courses – it's a great way to make sure you've spoken to all your guests

- Don't drink too much – you want to remember your day!

- Remember flat shoes for dancing

- Dry the bottom of your flowers before you pick them up – nobody wants a water stain on their dress

- Stay off the red wine... red wine and white wedding dresses don't mix!

- Have a bottle of water to hand in the wedding car

- Find your restroom-buddy (especially if your dress is hard to get into / out of)

- Smile – even if things don't go to plan if you're smiling, your whole bridal party will smile with you!

- Enjoy! The most wonderful and special day of your life is about to begin